Introduction to Adding and Taking Away

This book will help you to introduce your child to the idea of adding numbers of objects together and taking some away. Children show an interest in adding up and taking away at different ages. Whatever stage your child is at, using this book and watching the DVD together will be an enjoyable and rewarding experience.

The book contains:

- an introduction to key words: *more* and *less*

- opportunities for your child to practise adding more and taking some away

- activities where children count in twos and fives, as they repeatedly add two or five more

- a track game on page 22 in which children can practise their new skills.

Using the pack

The pack contains a DVD of clips taken from the BBC TV programme *Numbertime*. In many of the clips, Little Juan struggles with numbers, but the mysterious masked hero, El Nombre, swings in on his rope to save the day!

Enjoy completing t challenges of the p and watching the D introduce just one new idea at a time. Don't try to do too much in one go. Enjoy returning to favourite clips and pages as often as you like. This will help to develop confidence and secure earlier learning.

Included in this pack is a poster of colourful puzzles based on characters from the *Numbertime* programmes. Look at each pair of cards in turn and encourage your child to guess which card has more objects on it. This will help develop important skills of comparing and estimating. Check the guess by counting. Once your child is confidently identifying the card with more objects in each pair, work together to solve the puzzle of how many more there are.

> ### Hint
> Enjoy finding opportunities to talk about addition and subtraction in everyday life. For example, count the buttons on a coat as you fasten them.

Talking about adding

There are more words used to talk about adding than you might think. Words such as *more*, *add*, *too*, *another* and *altogether* are all about adding. Look for opportunities to use these words in everyday situations:

'I have put one egg in the mix, can you add one too?'

'Here is one sock, can you find another? We need one more.'

'Now, how many spoons do we have altogether?'

Early adding at home

The simplest way to introduce adding is just to count a small number of objects, perhaps when laying the table or putting biscuits on a plate. Count the biscuits, saying the final number, then add one more and say the new total. Reinforce the counts: 'We had four biscuits and put on one more. Now there are five. Four and one more makes five altogether'.

Later, children will be ready to add by counting on. Make a short line of toy cars and count them. 'We have one, two, three, four, five cars.' Now explain that three more cars are going to join the queue. Remind your child that you had five, keep your finger on car number five, and then count on as the new cars are added: 'Now we have five... six, seven, eight cars!'.

In this way, your child will learn that counting on is an important way of solving problems of addition.

Counting in twos and fives

On pages 14 and 15 you will see activities that encourage your child to count in twos and fives. Learning the patterns of counting in twos and fives can be great fun, and children learn that this can be a very quick way of counting large numbers of objects.

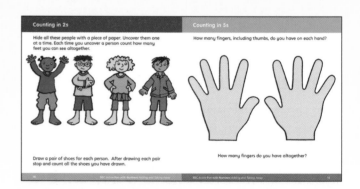

Talking about taking away

One of the best ways to introduce the idea of taking away is to sing nursery number songs together. 'Five little ducks went swimming one day', 'Five little speckled frogs' and 'Five currant buns in a baker's shop' are all songs about taking away.

As you sing the songs, encourage your child to hold up fingers to represent the decreasing number left, and talk about what is happening: 'You've taken one away! How many are left?'

Later on, your child will learn that counting backwards can help to solve taking away problems.

Early taking away at home

Look for opportunities to use the language of taking away at home: as you take plates from the table through to the kitchen, as you take a cake from a plate or as you put socks in the washing bag. Count the objects, talk about taking one away and then counting the number left: 'We had four cakes. Gran ate one, now there are three. Four, take away one, leaves three.'

More and less

Another useful skill to practise at home is that of comparing two groups of objects and saying which has more and which has less. Make a pretend toys' picnic with two teddies and share out tiny biscuits: 'Do both teddies have the same amount? Does one of them have more?' Line up the biscuits for each bear: 'Is one line longer? This teddy has one more than that one. This teddy has one less than that one.'

Go to page 24 for more top tips.

How many skittles are in each box? Draw 1 more skittle in each box.

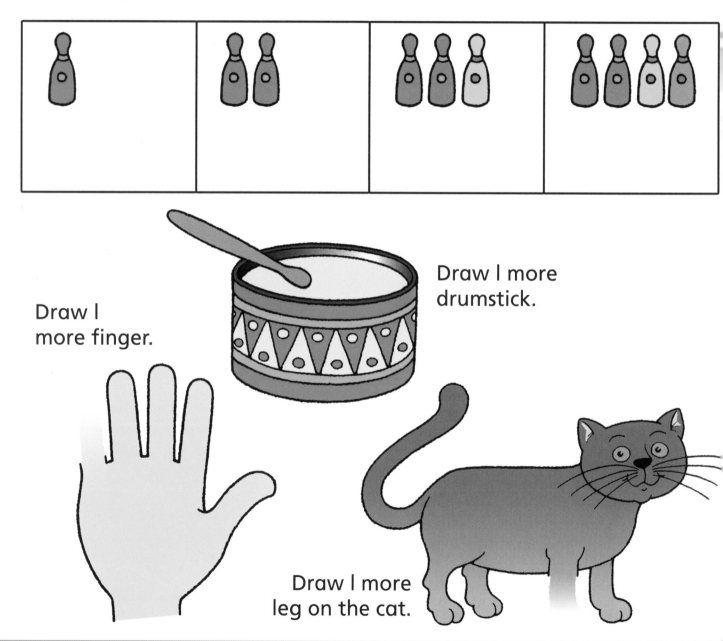

Draw 1 more
drumstick.

Draw 1
more finger.

Draw 1 more
leg on the cat.

How many tomatoes are there? Draw 2 more tomatoes.

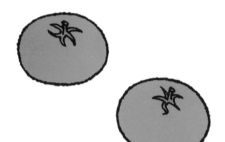

Draw 2 more socks.

Draw 2 more fish.

Draw I more footprint with 3 toes. How many toes are there now?

Draw 3 more apples.

Draw 3 more ice creams

How many spots are there on each ladybird? Draw 4 more spots on each ladybird.

Count how many spots there are now on each ladybird.

Draw 4 more legs on the octopus.

Draw 4 more petals on the flower.

Draw 1 more starfish with 5 legs. How many legs are there now?

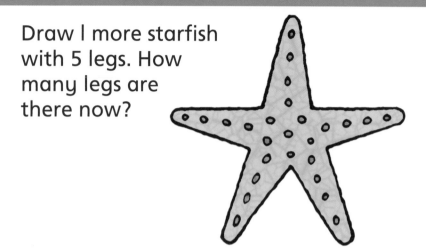

Draw 5 more eggs. How many eggs are there now?

Draw 5 more tarts. How many tarts are there now?

Count the mugs. Hide 1 with your hand.
How many mugs can you see now?

Count the flowers. Hide 1 with your hand.
How many flowers can you see now?

Here are some fruits and vegetables on a stall.

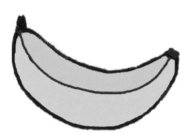  

Buy 2 bananas. How many will be left?

Buy 2 melons.
How many will be left?

Buy 2 carrots.
How many will be left?

Take away 3

The wind has blown 3 leaves from the tree.
Draw the leaves that are left.

Count the eggs.
Use 3 to make
a cake.

Draw the eggs
that are left.

Count the
brushes.
Use a crayon
to paint 3
of them.
How many
clean brushes
are left?

Count the books on the shelf. Cover 4 of them with your hand. How many can you see now?

Pretend to blow out 4 candles on the cake. How many candles are still alight?

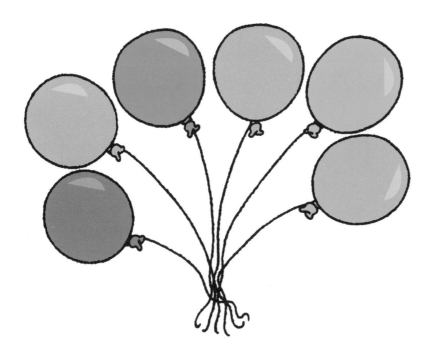

Count the balloons. Pretend to burst 5 of them. How many are left?

Count all the bottles. Hide 5 of them with your hand. How many can you see now?

Hide all these people with a piece of paper. Uncover them one at a time. Each time you uncover a person count how many feet you can see altogether.

Draw a pair of shoes for each person. After drawing each pair stop and count all the shoes you have drawn.

How many fingers, including thumbs, do you have on each hand?

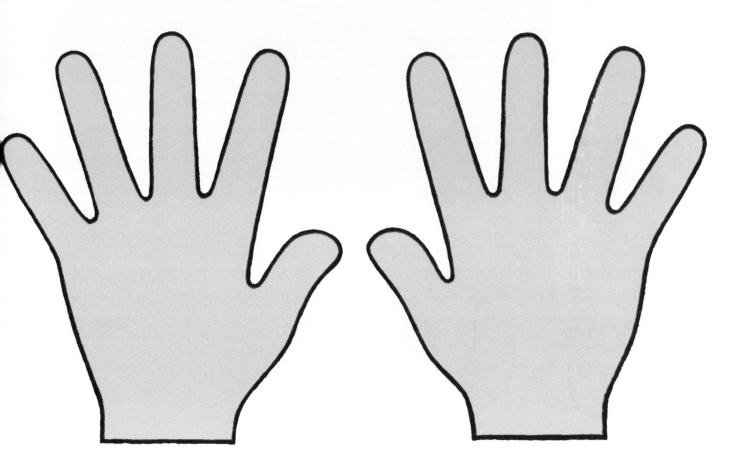

How many fingers do you have altogether?

More and less

Who has more apples, Jess or Lisa? How many more does she have?

Jess

Lisa

Who has more bananas, Jess or Lisa? How many more does she have?

Jess

Lisa

More and less again

Which box has more lemons in each row?

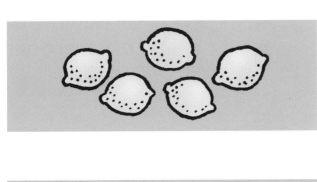 

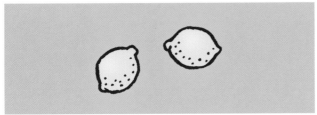 

 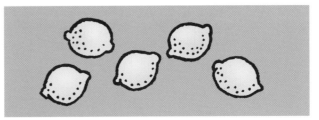

 How many
El Nombre dolls
are there here?

 How many
El Nombre dolls
are there here?

 How many dolls are
there altogether?

Draw I more. Count to find the total.

Count both sets and write the total in the box.

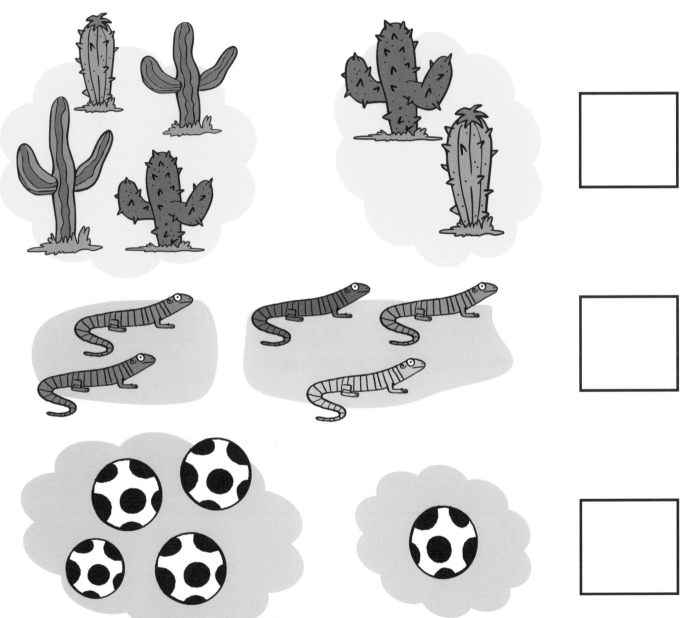

Max had 5 chocolate bars.

He ate 2 of them. How many bars are left?

Count how many. Cross out 1. How many are left?

More taking away

Write how many are left.

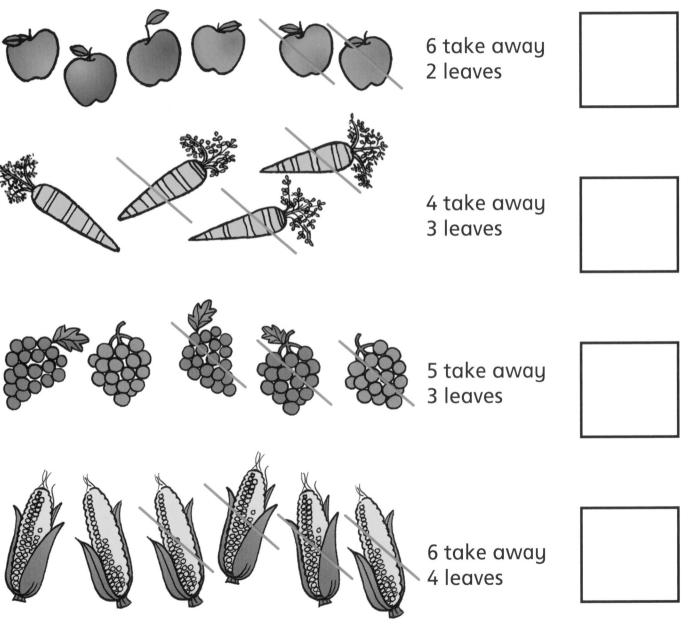

6 take away
2 leaves

4 take away
3 leaves

5 take away
3 leaves

6 take away
4 leaves

Counting on

Use your finger to help the frog make I jump.
Where will he land?

START

4

Go to 6.

3

Where is he
now?

2

5

1

Make 2 more jumps.

6

Make 2 more
jumps. Where is
the frog now?

7

8

Make 2 more
jumps. Where is
the frog now?

q

10

Number line

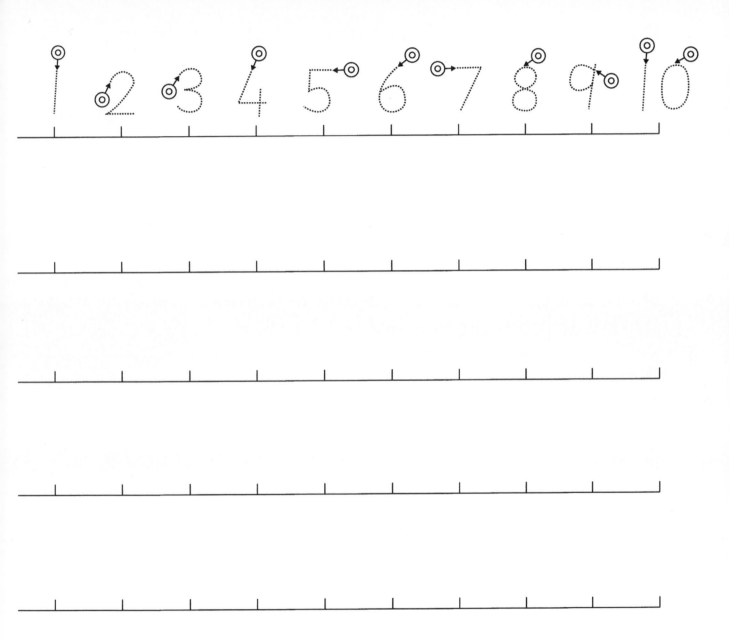

Top tips for learning at home

- Explain that this book and DVD are about adding numbers of things together and taking them away.

- Choose a time when both you and your child feel relaxed and comfortable.

- Playing is the best way to help young children to learn to enjoy numbers and to enjoy the puzzles of adding them together and taking some away.

- Share the gentle humour of the El Nombre *Numbertime* stories. It is good to laugh!

- Remember that little and often is the best recipe for success.

- Give plenty of praise and encouragement. Learning is about 'having a go'.

- Remember to stop when it becomes clear that your child is tiring.

- Always make sure that learning together is an enjoyable and playful experience!